Piper an

Minnie goes ...ng

Written and illustrated by Hannah Whyman-Naveh

Piper couldn't wait to put her boots on. It was her favourite time of the day, morning time, when Mummy mucks out the stables.
Piper sat on the floor next to the back door pulling on her bright pink wellies.

As usual, Minnie the chicken was outside waiting for Piper.
"Come on Minnie, we need to muck out!" said Piper, very excitedly.

"We need a wheelbarrow and a fork, Minnie" said Piper whilst pointing at the tools which were much bigger than her.
Minnie was very happy to be helping Piper.

Piper rushed with the tools into the stable to begin. She lifted all the dirty straw up with her fork and put it into the wheelbarrow.

The straw was very heavy!

"This is tricky, Minnie" said Piper in a sleepy voice, while turning to her friend who was nowhere to be seen. Hang on, that's odd, thought Piper. Where has Minnie gone?

Is she under this bucket? No.

Is she in the trailer? No.

Is she in the hen house? No.

Is she in with Spartacus the sheep? No.

Piper was getting very worried about where her best friend had gone.
She had searched the whole farmyard and Minnie was nowhere to be seen.
Suddenly, Piper heard a chirpy noise coming from the stable.

"Oh, there you are Minnie, you cheeky Chicken!"
Minnie had been fast asleep in the wheelbarrow the whole time.

Piper decided that was enough mucking out for one day. Cuddling Minnie was a much better use of her time.

The end.

*For my three beautiful
girls, Poppy, Indie
and Piper x*

Lightning Source UK Ltd.
Milton Keynes UK
UKHW021846160720
366634UK00006B/76